given to thomas and anne - August 8, 1978
as an accompanying wedding gift from
the daniel Joseph Gormans with two
Curraghmore champagne glasses

THE INCREDIBLE WATERFORD® CONTEST BOOK

Published by Portfolio Press
R.D. I
Huntington, New York 11743

Copyright © 1978 by

Waterford Glass, Inc., U.S.A.
Harry Pesin
Portfolio Press

Manufactured in the United States of America

Printed by Kenner Printing   First Edition

THE INCREDIBLE WATERFORD® CONTEST BOOK

An impulsive competition conceived by Harry Pesin.

Published by
Portfolio Press

It tapped a secret reservoir of creative expression and contributed a new body of lore to the old Waterford legend.

When it pours,

It all started in a sea of tranquility.
But in no time, it raged into a torrent.
The incredible Waterford contest.

How did it begin?
I had just written what I hoped would be a serenely elegant advertising campaign for Waterford Crystal. It revolved around four headlines:

1. "A water goblet by Waterford is not for water alone."
2. "Man lives not by water alone."
3. "How does your crystal garden grow?"
4. "When it pours, it reigns."

Not even the trace of a suggestion of a contest in any of these.

The photography was shot, the copy was on its way to the typographer.

The incredible Waterford contest was never actually conceived as a contest.

It was an impulsive addendum.

At the last moment, I thought it might be interesting to involve some competitive souls in the creative process, and added a line at the very end, asking readers to contribute their own ideas, verbally or pictorially. The proposal was put forth in tiny type to catch the eye of only the most persistent observer. I expected no more than a few hundred submissions at best, and, at first, even directed all mail to my own post office box. That was a mistake.

Shortly, very shortly after the first ad broke, I knew something was up.
People seemed to be impelled to tell us
how they weaved Waterford into their lives.
Driven to express the creative
impulse that stirred in them.

Poetry, pictures, paintings poured in by special delivery, registered mail, certified, stamped & sealed. Often, even the envelopes, boxes and packages came embellished with flashes of inspiration. They came from Brooklyn, Saudi Arabia, Israel; from Paris, Portugal, Peoria. They came from surgeons, lawyers, priests, professors, even U.S. Senate staffers.

In the end, the campaign attracted in excess of 50,000 entries, the best of which we publish here.

When it pours,

Own a pet Waterford Goblet and see the world!

My pet Waterford goblet would be my traveling companion. I would share all the world has to offer with my pet Waterford goblet: treat it to scotch in Scotland, ale in England, whiskey in Ireland, schanpps in Germany, wine in France, vodka in Russia, and so on around the world.

My Waterford goblet would be the perfect companion. It would travel light, never complain, and be a loyal friend.

Bon Voyage!

Anne

RED STAR

INGREDIENTS:

- 1 GREEN CHILE
- 1 PEELED TOMATO
- 1 12-OUNCE CAN TOMATO JUICE
- SALT
- LEMON WEDGE

INSTRUCTIONS:

WASH THE SEEDS FROM THE CHILE
PUREE THE CHILE IN BLENDER.
BLEND IN THE PEELED TOMATO.
BLEND IN TOMATO JUICE,
    A LITTLE AT A TIME.
SALT TO TASTE.
POUR IN GLASS; GARNISH WITH
    LEMON SLICE

GREEN CHILES HOT

Shroab el Loz (Milk of almonds)

1½ cups freshly ground almonds
3¾ cups water
4 cups sugar
2 tablespoons orange blossom or rose water

Prepare the milk of the almonds by soaking them in the water in a large bowl for an hour, rubbing and squeezing them, until no more milk can be extracted. This is more easily accomplished by putting the almonds first in a bag made of cheesecloth. The almond milk is then added to the sugar in a saucepan, to prepare the syrup, which is heated until it just starts to boil. The rose water or orange blossom water is added just after removing the pan from the heat. The syrup is cooled and stored in clean, dry bottles.
To serve, it is mixed with iced water, diluted to taste.

It is a most refreshing, fragrant, and beautiful drink.

THE QUESTION

AH! WHAT SHALL I POUR INTO THIS CRYSTAL SO CLEAR?

A RUBY RED WINE? A COLD FROTHY BEER?
THE JUICE OF A FRUIT WOULD BE VERY NICE,
OR MAYBE SPRING WATER, POURED OVER ICE.

A SCREWDRIVER, A SLING, A FLIP, OR SOME WINE
WOULD BE GREATLY ENHANCED IN THIS CRYSTAL DEVINE,
A CREME DE MENTHE FRAPPE SO GREEN, SO COOL??

GEE!!! I WISH I HAD GONE TO MIXOLOGISTS SCHOOL
IN ORDER TO ADD THAT ELEGANT TOUCH
TO SODA OR MILK, ICED COFFEE & SUCH
I'D DECANT ALL OF MY DRINKS, BOTH FANCY & PLAIN
INTO GOBLETS BY WATERFORD--AM I BEING TOO VAIN?

PAUL MOSMAN

REFLECTIONS OF A WATERFORD CRYSTAL DECANTER

Waterford, Waterford, where've you been?
  I've been to London to serve the Queen;
I've sat in the presence of nobles and earls
  And reflected the shimmer of diamonds and pearls.

I've cradled ruby claret for a cosmonaut's cup
  And decanted pale ouzo where jet setters sup.
I've rivaled the brilliance of chandeliers' gleam
  And shattered into rainbows a candle's warm beam.

I've basked in the touch of a butler's white glove,
  And known the delight of connoisseurs' love.
I've dwelt among the rich and the genteel poor
  All over the globe from Juneau to Groote Shuur.

I bring all who own me a great deal of pleasure,
  For I am unequalled --- a beauty, a treasure.
I realize no boundaries of distance or time,
  For I am forever, now and always, sublime.

                    Margaret Ann Thomas

Waterford Drink Ideas
P O. Drawer 350
Rancho Sante Fe, Ca   92067

Gentlemen:

I am sure you are aware that "thin is in." Therefore
I am on a perpetual diet.

I have in my possession one Waterford crystal goblet in
the Lismore pattern, which helps me forget the ever present
feeling of deprivation. How you ask? The recipe for my
special elixir is simple to prepare but the reward is great.

GRAND ILLUSION

Have on hand one nine ounce Waterford crystal
goblet. Place one thin slice of fresh lime in
the goblet. Add eight ounces of iced Perrier
water or similar sparkling mineral water. If you
feel daring add a maraschino cherry. Now sit
back, gaze at the irridescent beauty of it all
and then begin to sip slowly while thinking
happy thoughts. A thought to be considered is
your next vacation trip to Paris, Rio or Timbuktu.
For something close at hand you might contemplate
a visit to your favorite apparel shop, preferably
within the next twenty-four hours. This is a
non-sexist drink. It works for males and females.

So you see I do almost live on water alone with your help.

Yours truly,

Doris A. Feczko

Gentlemen:

Being a most avid "fan" and small-scale collector of Waterford crystal, I was intrigued by your advertisement in the New Yorker asking the reader to suggest a drink to be held by the crystal of crystals.

I have created a drink which I shall christen the "Waterford" Crystal Delight, named for Waterford which is the "crystal of light." I have used ingredients which are clear to maintain the beautiful reflective quality of the crystal. My suggestion is as follows:

THE WATERFORD CRYSTAL DELIGHT

2 oz. Vodka
½ oz. White Creme de Cacao
½ oz. White Creme de Menthe

Stir ingredients and pour over ice cubes. Garnish with an orange slice and a maraschino cherry pierced by a white swizzle stick. (The garnish incorporates the colors of the Irish flag.)

I am also enclosing a graphic representation of how the Crystal Delight might appear. I have used the Kylemore pattern which is my favorite stemware pattern. Let me also take time to congratulate Waterford for the beautiful ad in the May 16, 1977 issue of the New Yorker picturing the Alana Heirloom Wine Decanter on the inside cover. It's really an eye-catcher!

Thank you for this opportunity to participate in a campaign to publicize Waterford crystal.

Sincerely,

Robert D Stelch

The "Waterford" Crystal Delight

Dear Sirs:

When 17 year old João Bartolomeo d'Andrade left Funchal on the Atlantic island of Madeira in 1899, he was leaving his home forever. From his father's house along the bouganvilla filled Ribeira he took very little. He knew that he needed only his own courage and strength and ingenuity to begin an adult life in California. But he did bring with him three bottles of Madeira wine.

João sailed to Capetown, South Africa, and spent 2 years there working in restaurants. Then he continued his voyage across the world, past India and through the Tasmanian Sea, finally landing in Oregon. By then he had even fewer possessions, but still the three bottles of Madeira. These he carefully stowed in a canvas sack as he worked his way south on the Southern Pacific railroad to San Francisco. There, João, my grandfather, settled down to marry and raise a family.

Today, 10 years after his death, our family still hoards the last of grandpa's wine bottles. My father had it, a Câmara do Lobos, Veiga Franca, in its special place in his well stocked San Francisco cellar.

That is the drink I would like to pour, someday on a proper and fitting family occasion, into glasses of Waterford crystal.

Sincerely,

Florian M. Andrade

Florian M. Andrade

Dear Waterford,

I have a wonderful idea for
an unusual use for a Waterford goblet.
I have an official American League
baseball personally autographed by
Harmon Killebrew, former slugging
star of the Minnesota Twins. It is
inscribed: "To Jerry, Best Wishes,
Harmon Killebrew." One would think
that owning such a baseball would
make my life complete. Alas, I lack
a pedestal for my baseball. How
marvellous it would be to have my
baseball cradled by a fine Waterford
goblet. I hope you will agree.

Thank you for your consideration.

Yours,

Jerry Evan Kelley

Jerry Evan Kelley

DRINK IDEAS FOR WATERFORD ~...~...~ CRYSTAL ...~...

by michelle leblanc

" THE " CRANBERRY SPINNER

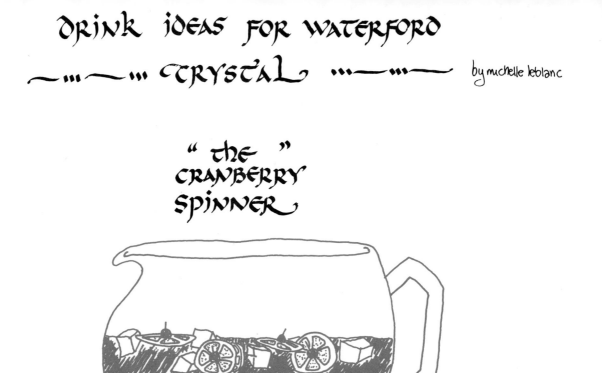

SPINNERS

CRANBERRY JUICE - 6 OZ. -
JUICE OF ONE HALF LEMON -
SPINNERS MADE FROM
LEMON SLICES, CRAN-
BERRYS, AND TOOTH-
PICKS - LEMON INSIDES
TURN LOVELY PINK -
ADD ICE ...~...~

" the "
STRAWBERRY cloud

"minted magic"

BLEND TOGETHER 6 OZ.
STRAWBERRY OR PEACH
FROZEN YOGURT AND 2 OZ
MANGO JUICE ~ TOP
WITH STRAWBERRY SLICES
DELICIOUS ... —— ... ..

ONE SHOT OF CREME DE MENTHE
ONE SHOT OF CREME DE COCAO
ONE SHOT OF BRANDY
BREYERS NATURAL MINT CHOCOLATE
CHIP ICE CREAM (3 SCOOPS OR
MORE)
MILK TO THIN DOWN TO DESIRED
CONSISTENCY ... —— ... ..

17

MICHAEL N. BURLESON, M.D.

A Waterford vase
In my personal taste
Holds tongue depressors
In elegant taste

Such use of the vase
May give one pause
Its purpose is simple
It produces more "ahs".

- as the moving piece for an autoscope (commercially known as Ouija Board) Make the alphabet on oiled cloth, invent the goblet, place fingers on the base and what have you got - the world's most prestigious soothsayer.

A sprig of wisteria
Had a fit of hysteria
Nearly blew its pistil
When put in a glass
Which wouldn't pass
For a piece of Waterford Crystal.

THE EXPLORERS CLUB

THE PHILADELPHIA CHAPTER
DOUGLAS C. THOMPSON, Chairman
OFFICE OF ADMISSIONS
SWARTHMORE COLLEGE
SWARTHMORE, PA. 19081

TELEPHONE
215-544-7900 (x446)
RES. 215-544-6898

April 25, 1977

Waterford Drink Ideas
Rancho Santa Fe CA 92067

Dear Sirs:

In response to your recent advertisement entitled "Man Lives Not By
Water Alone," I would like to submit my favorite drink to grace a
Waterford goblet. I learned to love this particular concoction during
two and one half years spent doing scientific research(cosmic ray physics)
in the Antarctic, and am pleased to send it for your perusal.

PLEISTOTINI

1 oz.	190 proof grain alcohol
1/2 oz.	melted Antarctic glacier ice
1/8 drop	Extract of Juniper Berries
1/4 oz.	Dry Vermouth

garnish with green olives or a lemon twist if available and
pour over chipped 50,000 year old Antarctic glacier ice.

A few notes may be in order to explain the distinctive features of the
PLEISTOTINI. The name is derived from the Pleistocene era when snow fell
to earth and formed the ice that is used in the drink. The ice, and the
water derived from it, are of unusual clarity since there were no man-made
pollutants in the air 50,000 years ago. The clarity and brillance of the
ice serve to set off the clarity and brillance of the Waterford crystal in
in which it should reside. The biology laboratory serves as the source of
the excellent substitute gin described above if the usual variety is not
available, as is frequently the case at the South Pole. One interesting
feature of the ice is that it will frequently crackle and pop in the drink
due to compressed gasses contained within it, and this can add a delightful
sparkle to the potion.
My best wishes, and I hope you can use my favorite Waterford drink.

Yours truly,

Doug Thompson

19

The following items are suggested as something special to pour into Waterford crystal. The recipies are from my grandmother"s cook book. I have her punchbowl (which incidentally was buried during the Civil War to keep it out of the hands of the Yankees) It was told to me that the punch bowl was never empty, and stood on the front hall table as a gesture of hospitality to arriving guests. I quote the recipies exactly as set forthin the book. Some modernization could take place.

For the winter punch bowl: APPLE TODDY

Eight well baked red streaked apples
 One pint each: Peach brandy, Jamaica spirits, Santa Cruz rum,
        powdered sugar
Four quarts boiling water, ten cloves, ten allspice,six blades
of mace, half a grated nutmeg, half a teaspoon ground ginger,
two tablespoons pineapple syrup, four slices preserved pineapple.
When cold strain and keep in a cold place for two or three weeks.
Serve dhilled.
    When I have made this one I substituted fresh pineapple spears
    in each glass rather than the preserved pineapple. Serve
    this in a rather small Waterford crystal as it is pretty
    potent stuff

For the summer punch bowl: CONFEDERATE PUNCH

  In four tumblers of water dissolve two pounds of white sugar. Then
add four tumblers of sherry, two of brandy, two of rum and one of
lemon juice. Rub the rinds of two fresh lemons on some lumps of
sugar, being careful to take off all the yellow rind but none of the
white, which would make it bitter. Mix all thoroughly. The longer
it is kept the better it is. The bowl should be filled with cracked
ice or it will be too strong

For those who have a sufficiently elegant household to use
Waterford Crystal in the bathroom, I submit the following
  "Wash for the Teeth and Gums" Two ounces of the best Peruvian
bark, finely pulverized. Half a pint of old French brandy. Half
a pint of rose water. Half a pint of spring water. Mix all together
and in twenty four hours it is ready for use. For a severe tooth
ache add more brandy and hold in the mouth for five minutes. Use
frequently with a brush."

Ah, WATERFORD!

How do I drink from thee?   Let me count the ways.

Adoringly with Amaretto in *ADARE*
Affectionately with Asti Spumonti in *ASHLING*
Amorously with Anisette in *ALANA*
Beautifully with Benedictine in *BOYNE*
Caressingly with Campari in *CLARE*
Coyly with Cointreau in *CASHEL*
Compassionately with Curacao in *COMERAGH*
Celebratedly with Chenin Blanc in *CASTLETOWN*
Coquettishly with Cognac in *COLLEEN*
Deliciously with Drambuie in *DONEGAL*
Devotedly with Dubonnet in *DUNMORE*
Enjoyably with Echezeaux in *EILEEN*
Gregariously with Grasshoppers in *GLENGARRIFF*
Gaily with Galiano in *GALTEE*
Graciously with Gevrey-Chambertin in *GLENCREE*
Glamorously with Gimlets in *GLENMORE*
Kindly with Kirschwasser in *KILDARE*
Kaleidoscopically with Kahlua in *KATHLEEN*
Keenly with Kummel in *KENMARE*
Kittenishly with Kijafa in *KYLEMORE*
Kissingly with Kirsch in *KINSALE*
Lovingly with Lillet in *LISMORE*
Mellowly with Mead in *MAUREEN*
Passionately with Pernod in *POWERSCOURT*
Romantically with Rose in *ROSSLARE*
Sumptuously with Sherry in *SHEILA*
Tantalizingly with Tequila in *TEMPLEMORE*
Triumphantly with Tavel in *TRALEE*
Tenderly with Tia Maria in *TYRONE*
Theatrically with Triple Sec in *TRAMORE*, and

Culminatingly, in *CURRAGHMORE** anything tastes like champagne!

* *Why the preferential treatment for CURRAGHMORE ? Because, after two trips to Ireland and the Waterford factory, this is the pattern I selected for my very own!*

Let it be published,
Yes let it be known
That Waterford isn't
for water alone,
To grace just a table
set with china of bone

So think if you will
of some crystal
adventures,

And use a goblet to-
night when you're
soaking your
dentures!

"You've got to win that flask for me,"
     I heard her softly say,
"...so please think up some poetry
     and I'll be on my way."

To merely spout off banter
     requires little class
But to write on a decanter
     can pain a poet's glass.

Well, wat-er say? "Pour me," I cry,
     "A facet-ating task.
A spirit-less soliloquy
     about an empty flask."

Yet, I shan't wine. "Keep your gin up"
     (My conscience won't relax)
"You've quite enough wit-to-afford
     ad-verse-ity's attacks."

She returned to her sad man:
     The poet clear-ly failed.
Then, she ran off with the ad-man
     on whose art t'was I impaled.

So I drank, and left my stanzas
     with this moral to extol:
A full decanter in the hand's
     worth twelve upon the scroll.

THE EASTER BUNNY WOULD
DYE EASTER EGGS IN HIS
WATERFORD GOBLETS.

Images

Flowers from weeds, crystal from sand;
Alchemy chanced, alchemy planned.

Inn of garden guests room to room,
Open air inn, fixed as Brigadoon.

Waif,
Climb the crystal lattice,
Peer 'round the leaded panes.
You who whimsied stormy threats,
Or lay sway in dozing flight --
Now stand bound by a shadow,
Held fast by shafts of light.

Chink clad vase,
Woo the wistful, woo the murmer of the rain.
Put to sleep by weeping flowers,
By flowers' kiss awoke.
Babushka vase,
Wishing well in garland cloak.

Wedding ring about your finger stem,
Resigned consent,
One of this from two of them.

As starlit heavens caught your nightly gaze,
So catchlight vase shows stars by days.

Dream journey,
Water's sip the passport price.
Breathe your scented breath,
Face of fracted ice.

Empath elixor,
Gypsy bouquet on oracle sphere,
Eclipse the hour's care --
And show the work of a thousand years.

why not a tie-in
with prestige or FDA florists across the country - to use the goblet, tied with pink or
blue ribbon, as a floral container (fresh or
dried flowers) to be sent to new mothers after
their baby's arrival? As a corollary to this-
perhaps also a cordial glass for the baby!
This would be an expensive, though certainly
distinctive way of"saying it with flowers!"

   Also, what about the use of the Waterford
name in a song - preferably a ballad, to be
popularized by a top singer? "You're the Top"
did a lot for Bendel's, in New York!....Or
could the Irish Tourist Bureau incorporate
in some of its radio or TV advertising, here
in the USA, the name of Waterford - hopefully
set to music?

                    Sincerely yours,

                    Rivena Holmes

                    (Mrs.Volney M.Holmes)

GOBLET IDEAS

Waterford easily conjures up
The way we all would like to sup!
Birthdays, holidays --occasions all!
Waterford creates its waterfall.

Tables sparkle, linens glisten.
Silver gleams and hostess beams!
What a pleasure, what a ploy...
A charm to see, to use..a joy!!

What's to do when such time passes?
Do not hide those wonderful glasses!!
Born in fire, blown by mouth,
Cut by hand, with heart devout.

Let them capture their own way
a place in time, in style, each day.
Be it said, they serve "their way"
And what a privilege to use each day!

Holding flowers, milk or juice...
Catching sunbeams, serving mousse.
Place them casually through the house...
Use them always to toast your spouse!

Let yourself go, massage your psyche!
You'll use them often, wrong or rightly!
In the kitchen, in the hall,
Empty, full, you'll love it all.

The warmth, the notice, the special care
It took to have you place them there.

Have one near when on the phone;
"Man lives not by water alone"!
Holding pencils, strips of paper,
Always serving at your favor.

Only God can make a tree.....
But I'm so pleased you made Waterford for me!!

A perfect frog's egg is what I would put into a large Waterford
crystal goblet! It would be determined by a biologist to be an egg
which would hatch a male frog. All the right ingredients would be
put into the water with the egg to insure its healthy development.
When it grew into a tadpole, it would be moved to a large Waterford
crystal salad or punch bowl. When the frog became an adult, I would
have a beautiful, likable, young girl kiss him. A frog who grew up in
such elegant surroundings couldn't do anything but turn into a prince!

Alex

P.S. It is to be hoped that this beautiful, likable ,girl will be
grateful enough to send me a handsome gift of Waterford
crystal.

Good Day,

As a researcher engaged in the study of human viruses, I spend many hours each day in a laboratory that is, in a word, barren. Due to the strict sterility requirements, many decorations that might lend warmth or beauty to the room (e.g. plants) are forbidden. In addition, most of the glass apparatus which fills the room is autrociously ugly. If I had a pet Waterford Goblet, I would replace a beaker that is used daily to hold a number of small scrapers (used for collecting cultured cells) submerged in water. The real advantage of a Waterford goblet becomes apparent when one realizes that the scrapers and water are contaminated with the radioactive isotope we use in our studies. The superior lead content of the glass would shield those of us in the room from harmful radiation more effectively than any other glass. The goblet would, in effect, help maintain our physical health by its composition and our psychological health by its beauty. La double vie, n'est-ce pas?

Sincerely,

Dennis T. Drayna

Dennis T. Drayna

This is what I would do with a pet Waterford goblet.

Even though an adult, I like to blow soap bubbles. I have found a terrific kind made in West Germany. It has a unique wand and comes in a very attractive tube-shape container. It is a colorful red and blue with a teddybear pictured blowing bubbles. It would look fine in my pet Waterford goblet. Whenever I went to blow bubbles I would have the pleasure of seeing the soap bubble container, the bubbles when blown, and the beautiful goblet. All a delight to the eye

Sincerely yours,
J. M. Keaton

Rancho Santa Fe
California 92067

Dear Sirs:

If I had a Waterford goblet as a pet, I would use it for a nice water-tower for my model railroad. I would put it right in the middle of the rich section on my railroad layout. I would use an extra little hose to siphon the water into the train.

Sincerely,
Rod Arends

As a mathematics teacher, a Waterford goblet would serve as an inducement for a lesson, as well as provide concrete examples of conic sections for my students. I would bring the Waterford goblet to school, pass a light through it, and exhibit shadows of parabolas, hyperbolas and other functions for my class. The Waterford goblet would be a superb practical application of mathematical beauty in the real world.

Submitted by:

Angela C. Gallicchio, Ph.D.

Surely Waterford crystal abides most comfortably in a gracious and delightful setting. Hence, I offer both thanks and apologies to the estate of J. R. R. Tolkien and imagine thus:

A Waterford goblet filled to brim with a certain beverage of the Ents— the wise and noble trees of Fanghorn Forest. In The Two Towers we find it described:

"The drink was like water... and yet there was some scent or savour in it which they could not describe: it was faint, but it reminded them of the smell of a distant wood borne from a-far by a cool breeze at night. The effect of the draught began at the toes, and rose steadily through every limb, bringing refreshment and vigour as it coursed upwards, right to the tips of the hair." *

Blessings of hobbits and Elven-folk on your works.

Cheers!

Betty Wolfe

* The Two Towers by J. R. R. Tolkien. Ballentine Books, New York (1965), p. 93.

34

Enclosed is a recipe, called the "Waterford Waly".
I make and serve this in Waterford Crystal Cordial glasses.
My husband bought the Cordial glasses for our 25th.
wedding anniversay, and the following year, we bought the wine glasses.
I do not have water goblets and thought that I might give my recipe
for our drink, with a hope of being one of the hundred fortunate
winners.
Why should man live by water alone, when he can
have a Waterford Waly?
Waly is an adj. that means beautiful, pleasing,
strong and robust.
Enclosed also is the beautiful ad from my magazine,
that prompted this entry. Under seperate cover, will be a sample of
"Waterford Waly". Hope that you like it.
Yours truly,
Johanna Morrell R.N.R.T.

Waterford Waly . **serve in Waterford Cordials.**
Gallon glass jug and lid
3 pts. sour pie cherries - pitted. Place in
jug with 2 pts. granulated sugar and 1/5 Vodka.
Sit on kitchen shelf. Do not cover tightly
and allow for expansion. Each day shake jug
well, do this for 30 days. Pour off and strain
this mixture (very sweet) so re-use cherries,
adding 2 pts sugar and 1/5 more Vodka. Repeat
process. Strain off - mix the two batches
together and bottle in old liquor bottles.
Makes 4 bottles.

Johanna Morrell
A pretty color and sweet cherry taste.
Serve after dinner & during holidays.

My great aunt carried it with her,
On the boat.
My grandmother was three or four years old then,
She didn't remember much of the trip over,
She forgot most of Ireland.
She remembered riding in a cart pulled by goats,
She remembered the boys---
Her four older brothers---
Wanted to come here.
It was really their idea,
They came to work on the railroad,
One was killed on the railroad,
Seventeen years old,
The youngest son,
The youngest son,
The youngest son in an Irish family is the favorite son.
Dead.
It drove my great grandmother mad.
They were all dead before I was born,
I think,
All except my grandmother and the oldest boy
Mike.
Most of them buried near the railroad.

Somehow the pitcher came to me,
From my great aunt---
I can't even remember her name,
Dead before I was born.
I guess the pitcher passed to my mother
And then to me.
That must be the way it happened.
I know them all---

All the relatives who died before I was born.
I am linked to them,
Not just through genes
But through temperament.

What else did she bring with her---
My great aunt?
I think they brought very little from Ireland.
They probably thought they'd find it all
Here.
I hope they did.
I don't think they did.
It was probably the only piece of cut-glass they packed.
It may have been the only piece they owned.
The great crazy beauty of it,
To pack a lemonade pitcher
For an Atlantic crossing in steerage---
But it got here,
And is still here,
Seventy-two years after she thought to pack it,
Knowing or not knowing it would come to me---
Her great niece,
Born after she died,
Living far from the railroad where her brother died,
Living far from the family---
Or close to it---
Depending on how you look at things.
When she packed the Waterford pitcher,
Did she see it all?
Did she see me?

WATERFORD GANG:

I magine you are building a new home, or re-decorating an old, unexciting dining room. where does one start with a dining room? It should be comfortable, yet elegant; promote friendship, yet speak of good taste.

How about starting with the chandelier? And why not have it as unique as your individual personality? Here is one for starters:

Using 2x4 redwood beams & waterford goblets we create a unique design. Materials needed:

① 8 waterford glasses, ② 8 – 7" segments of natural redwood 2x4's, 2 grape stakes

③ 30 feet of natural-color cord, a plug, a dimmer switch, a socket, & a 150 watt frosted bulb; finishing nails, epoxy glue

In 2 sections we contruct the chandelier. The bottom uses 5 wood sections & 5 upside down goblets, & one grape stake

Top view:
goblet →
grape stake →
redwood 2x4

side view
2x4 →
grape stake   goblet fits here

the top section is the same, only with 3 each   top

side

connect the two with 3 – 9" lengths of grape stake & fasten to ceiling placket. Lower bulb & adjust dimmer switch! A new dining experience!

Jim Lusk

38

A NEW EXPERIENCE!

a waterford goblet chandelier!

A Hopeful Entry in the Waterford Goblet Ideas Race

During the current Lenten season, I have learned to do pysanky, the Ukrainian
egg art form. Having learned the process, I intend to practice yearround, for it
takes time to acquire skill, and to accumulate decorated eggs for one's own
collection and as gifts to others. In pysanky work, one etches or really "writes"
a design on the egg (an egg that has not been processed or preserved or preferably even washed) with beeswax, then dips the egg into dye, which colors all
but the waxed portions. To obtain the design complexity and color variants,
successive waxings and dye baths are used. Four traditional dye colors are
used, limited to natural dye colors Ukrainians could obtain: yellow, red,
blue and black.

I cannot think of any more entrancing or splurgy use of four Waterford water
goblets than as vessels for the pysanky dye baths. To see the egg, the beginning
of life, afloat in a vessel born of fire, seems appropriate and harmonious.
My own aspiration to create beauty in decorating the egg would be intensified
in the connection with the achieved and wondrous beauty of Waterford crystal.

(Mrs.) Marion M. Donovan

A Waterford Workbench

A workbench for the discerning home craftsman. Marble-topped with

Waterford goblets to hold nails, nuts, bolts and other essentials.

The workbench is lighted by an enormous Waterford goblet that throws

off bright light as the workmen is using his diamond-edged saw.

Always bring out your Waterford goblet if feeling blue: it's
safer than pills, cheaper than a psychiatrist and its beauty
and elegance make it spiritually uplifting, whether holding
mineral water, Pernod and water -- or chocolate milk.

Sincerely,

MARTHA MILLARD

The Dulany Mahan Memorial Garden beside the Mark Twain Home in Hannibal, Missouri. Given to the City by Mrs. Sara Mahan and children. The statue of Tom Sawyer was done by Walter Russell of New York. The roses and old-fashioned flowers bloom partly where the Clemens family (Mark's real name was Samuel Langhorne Clemens) had their own flowers and vegetables, and partly upon the site of the vanished Virginia Hotel.

There is a gent I just call Me,
Whose garden grows prolifically.
    When asked, "What lacks?",
    Two words, straight facts:
"Waterford, quintessentially."

Frederick J. Schultz

POST CARD

Waterford Crystal Garden
P.O. Box 1159
Rancho Santa Fe, CA.
        92067

There once was a Lady whose daughter would
Toss off beers in a way that a porter could.
She gilded the lily
By serving her filly
Her waterfront tastes in a Waterford.

Capturing Light Live

Waterford's white ovens spin flowing crystals
as the blower's hands swirl,
and bugle-cheeks bubble molten fire into chisled light;
sealed, symmetrical gleams
signed in asymmetrical strokes,
caressed in a vessel of splendor in your hand:
        an ephiphany beauty, firing forever.

A bachelor's button from Bristol

Was elegant, petal to pistil;

Picked just for the Queen,

She refused to be seen

Except in Her Waterford Crystal!

Said the rose to the thistle,
"Why do you whistle
at that weed that gives me the blahs?"

"That weed", replied thistle,
"has sparkle and sizzle
when placed in a Waterford vase."

Daisies won't tell

And seldom do well

Usually suffer from malaise

When placed in a jar

That is inferior by far

To a delicate Waterford vase.

If your Azalea should falea,

Have no fear!

If your Hydrangea can't stangea,

I am here.

If you can not afford to own a Waterford,

Please don't cry.

For my Forsythia will kithia,

And so will I!

Dear Waterford Drink Ideas,

I saw your ad in <u>House Beautiful</u> and was intrigued by it. I am a North Dakota housewife where the winters are long, the people are hardworking and friendly and the living style is still relatively simple, but how we do love beautiful things! They make our winters seem shorter in this wide open country where the wind blows continuously and the winters last for so much of the year.

I have given the idea of what I would pour into the Waterford crystal much thought. I have decided that I would love most to pour into this legendary crystal some fresh home churned pure white buttermilk, with tiny bits of butter floating on the top, sparkling amid the nourishing white milk just as the lovely Waterford crystal sparkles on the table. It was this once plentiful drink that was the mainstay of many of our meals while growing up during the depression years in Arkansas. I feel that fresh buttermilk would fit right into the style of living just now, which is going back to the simple living of the "Nostalgia years". Even the young people of today are nostalgic for an uncomplicated life which they have never had but can only yearn for.

Having been born & reared in the south during the depression years, I have tried to forget the hard times and remember the pleasant ones. One of the pleasant things of that era was the day of the week when we churned our butter. Everything was gotten ready and all of us children took our turns at the churn. How excited we were when we finally saw the butter gather at the top. The butter was ladled out by our mother and the dasher removed from the churn. At last, As a reward for our labors, we were allowed a glass of the buttermilk. No drink has ever tasted better than that first glass of buttermilk right out of the churn

Id like to drink a toast in sparkling Waterford Crystal to the times when buttermilk kept us from hunger during those long ago years. I am hoping you may find this idea interesting enough to help me start my set as I would dearly love to own them. They are truly beautiful.

Yours Sincerly,

Mrs. Joseph W. Beeler

Dear Sir:

May I submit the following "nose tingling" recipe for scuppernong wine that my husband makes. (It <u>has been</u> served in your Lizmore wine stems at my son's home, by the way.)

Scuppernong Wine

1 10 gallon wooden barrel with wooden spigot at the
      bottom. (Can be purchased and inserted)
1 bushel grapes,(scuppernongs)
15 pounds sugar
Crush grapes. Add enough water to come with in 4 inches of the top of the barrel.
Next bore a hole in the barrel lid and insert a piece of copper tubing, 5 in. long, to this attach a plastic tubing about 1 yard long, enough to reach to a gallon jug of water that is filled within 4 inches of the top. The mixture will ferment and the tube will show bubbles in the water as it works. When the above is all secure melt paraffin wax and pour over the lid, closing all air holes, sealing it air tight.

After about six weeks the bubbles will gradually stop and the wine is ready to pour out from the spigot. Store in bottles.

For more color add a quart of bottled grape juice. This is a sweet, effervescent wine. Suitable even for champagne glasses.

Thanks,

Dorothy P. Goodnight
Mrs. A. H. Goodnight

Yield: 14 gallons

VERBAL HERBAL

They put herbs in shampoos,
    In creams and ▰ perfumes.
There are herbs to spray
    In stuffy rooms;
And herbs that season
    Our sauces and meat;
Plus herbs to whiff,
    To apply or to eat.
But in a Waterford vase
    The herb's really a jewel,
Playing its role . . .
    In herban renewal.

A Few Notes On Evolution
Of A Certain Kind

In the long, long procession
Of lovers of wine
And the myriad spirits
Of whatever kind,

There even were kings
(At least so they say),
Who swigged from the
Bottle directly (dismay!).

Now, everyone knows that
That isn't quite nice -
(It was long, long ago, though,
Please be adviced).

However, the point is that
Even though wine,
And spirits and potables
Each of their kind,

Had all been developed
To utmost delight,
The vessels that held them
Were mostly a fright.

You could find all you wanted
Of goatskins and pots,
Of mugs and of jars
Made of clays and whatnots.

So although they were greeted
With welcoming clamor,
Those magical drinks were
Served without glamour -

Poured into glasses
(They had them by then)
So plain and prosaic
You couldn't tell when

Your host was a bourgeois
Or really a swell,
And with some folks in those days
That didn't sit well.

Well, enough was enough,
And there rose a small band
Of artists who conjured up
Crystal by hand,

And leaded and shaped it and
Carved it and wrought,
Till it glowed with the beauty
Of jewels long sought.

And all at once, elegance
Reigned at the board,
And people were mesmerized
When their host **poured**.

Goblets and glasses
(No more in disdain)
Were prized with a passion
That brought them to fame.
And what were they named,
This world-renowned blaze
Of crystal creations
So graceful to raise -

Decanters and glasses
No longer ignored,
Acclaimed and accepted,
Were called Waterford.

L'envoi

So it was and now is,
With all in accord.
To use the vernacular,
Waterford scored.

'THE TRIANGLE'

© DAN & SCOTT TUCKER 1977

1oz. COCKSPUR RUM
1oz. BLACK SEAL RUM
1oz. 151 RUM

Top with OJ & Pineapple Juice
Garnish with Cherry & Orange Slice.

THIS IRISHMAN'S DREAM

A little bit of h'ven fell from out the sky
And nestled in a glass of Waterford.
As I tasted its perfection I was wont to try
To analyze the feelin' that filled me with accord.

I could distinguish so many things
From deep down places and darkened recesses,
My mind was spinning and my heart grew wings,
And I was moved to imagining's excesses.

I could see an isle of emerald green,
And rolling hills and bright mirrored lakes,
And houses, thatched roofed and pure white clean.
And then I knew that these an earthly h'ven makes.

I sensed a people - at once new, yet centuries old.
I saw long-time suppression and freedom hard won.
They had heavy shoulders, set straight and bold,
And eyes that marked them as a nation one.

But love was there, and mirth, and joy, and song.
They had compassion from one to one and each to each
That made them feel that they surely did belong
To a God who could not be beyond their reach.

And so these thoughts I dreamed as I did drink
A bit of h'ven from my Waterford clear.
I soon was overtaken with the feeling pink
That shrouded me from hate and pain and fear.

Gentlemen:

      My conception of an irresistable use of Waterford crystal would be a weekend tasting of great red wines. My ideal Waterford weekend begins with a Friday evening vertical tasting of Heitz -- and, in particular, a generous selection of Martha's Vineyard--Cabernet Sauvignon, to be followed on Saturday evening with a vertical tasting of Chateau Latour. This glorious weekend would be concluded Sunday evening with two great Burgundies from the 1961 vintage -- Le Chambertin and Romanée-Conti. Do I ask too much?

                                     Very truly yours

                                     W. P. Grant

WATERFORD
IS
BEAUTIFUL !
.
.
IT
CAN
FLY.......

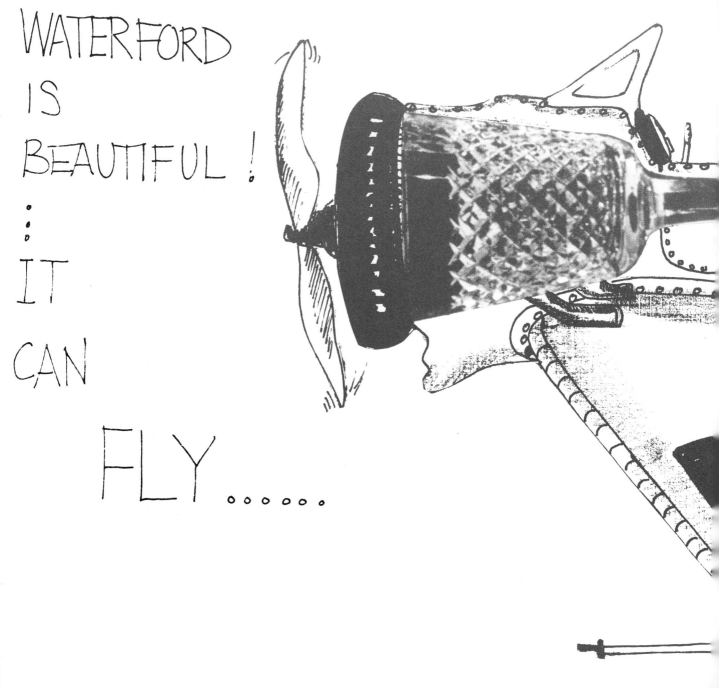

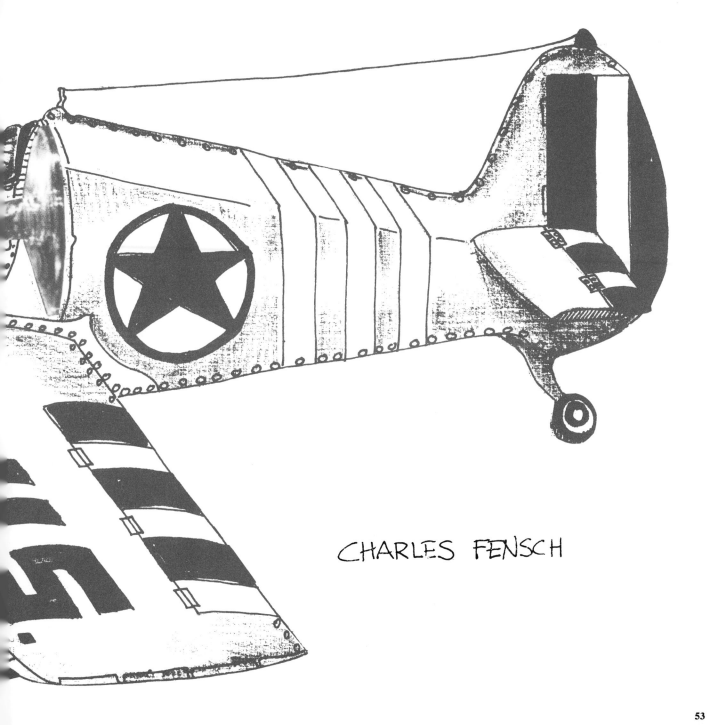

CHARLES FENSCH

Into this legendary Waterford crystal
I would pour out
From the decanter's of the physician of the
Olympic Gods,
Paens to patriotism and ancient piety
which free spirits infuse belief.

As the liquor cascades down the paens of
crystal time
it liberates the rainbow fused into glass
and reflects back,
the scarred columns of Faith, invigoratingly
and prisms off the shield like blue surface
of Virtue, of help vouchsafed, and stirs up
the sovereign Freedom,
as its soaring up and forward needs to be
drunk as prescribed.

Gentle Persons,

    As I pour wine or water into Waterford
crystal the above song always flows out or
some such tuneful dance music for rainbows.

Thanx,   Francise Mostronthy

Dear Artists:

The Gothic architecture of the beautiful campus of Duke University was the inspiration for this elegant party punch.

It is called Gothic Punch because, like the spires of a breathtaking Gothic cathedral, it will make party guests "rise up to soaring heights!"

* *

GOTHIC PUNCH

4 bottles Sauterne
1 bottle Claret
1 bottle Champagne
1 cup fresh orange juice, strained
1/2 cup granulated sugar

Dissolve sugar in orange juice and add to the wine. Let stand 1 hour. Pour over a frozen strawberry-mint ice ring in a punch bowl. (Waterford, of course). Just before serving, add the Champagne which has been chilled.

Ice ring: Pour about 1/2 inch of water into a ring mold. When it is partly frozen, add fresh strawberry halves and fresh mint sprigs. Freeze. Keep adding a little water, strawberries and mint, freezing after each addition until mold is filled. Store in freezer. Unmold just before serving punch.

* *

Gothic Punch would love to be poured into Waterford champagne glasses, wine glasses, punch cups or any of the lovely-to-hold fine crystal.

The classic beauty of legendary Waterford and legendary Gothic go together.

At Duke University we believe in the correlation of the arts!

Sincerely yours,

Mary Beach

Mary Beach (Mrs. Waldo)

I believe that water is most suitable for this legendary Waterford crystal. Why? Because of

Its universality: its democratic equality and constancy to its nature in seeking its own level: its vastness in the ocean of Mercator's projection: its umplumbed profundity in the Sundam Trench of the Pacific exceeding 8,000 fathoms: the restlessness of its waves and surface particles visiting in turn all points of its seaboard: the independence of its units: the variability of states of sea: its hydrostatic quiescence in clam: its hydrokinetic turgidity in neap and spring tides: its subsidence after devastation: its sterility in the circumpolar icecaps, arctic, and antarctic: its climatic and commercial significance: its preponderance of 3 to 1 over the dry land of the globe: its indisputable hegemony extending in square leagues over all the region below the subequatorial tropic of Capricorn: the multisecular stability of its primeval basin: its luteofulvuous bed: its capacity to dissolve and hold in solution all soluble substances including millions of tons of the most precious metals: its slow erosions of peninsulas and downwardtending promonotories: its alluvial deposits: its weight and volume and density: its imperturbability in lagoons and highland tarns: its gradation of colours in the torrid and temperate and frigid zones: its vehicular ramifications in continental lakecontained streams and confluent oceanflowing rivers with their tributaries and transoceanic currents: gulfstreams, north and south equatorial courses: its violence in seaquakes, waterspouts, artesian wells, eruptions, torrents, eddies, freshets, spates, groundswells, water sheds, waterpartings, geysers, cataracts, whirlpools, maelstroms, inundations, deluges, cloudbursts: its vast circumterrestrial ahorizontal curve: its secrecy in springs, and latent humidity, revealed by rhabdomantic or hygrometric instruments and exemplified by the hole in the wall at Ashtown gate, saturation of air, distillation of dew: the simplicity of its composition, two constituent parts of hydrogen with one constituent part of oxygen: its healing virtues: its buoyancy in the waters of the Dead Sea: its perservering penetrativeness in runnels, gullies, inadequate dams, leaks on shipboard: its properties for cleansing, quenching thirst and fire, nourishing vegatation: its infallibility as paradigm and paragon: its metamorphoses as vapour, mist, cloud, rain, sleet, snow, hail: its strength in hydrants: its variety of forms in loughs and bays and gulfs and bights and guts and lagoons and atolls and archipelagos and sounds and fjords and minches and tidal esturaies and arms of sea: its solidity in glaciers, icebergs, icefloes: its docility in working hydraulic millwheels, turbines, dynamos, electric power stations, bleachworks, tanneries, scutchmills: its utility in canals, rivers, if navigable, floating and graving docks: it's potentiality derivable from harnessed tides or watercourses falling from level to level: its submarine fauna and flora (anacoustic, photophobe) numerically, if not literally, the inhabitants of the globe: its ubiquity as constituting 90% of the human body.

(James Joyce, Ulysses, pp 655-656)

Sincerely,

Michael Diamond

56

Lismore

Not by water alone lives man
Man who forms his world with craft
Artfully spinning his hopes and dreams
In visions of crystal which portray
Images of his children, his wife
His life he has chosen. He toasts,
Toasts with a fine wine in sparkling glass,
Crystal crafted to enhance a warm liquor
Warm fluid to enrich a special moment
Or thoughtful silence with the breath of life,
A life he lives not by water alone

A crystal goblet, shaped from endless molten alternatives,
Fired hard as flint, yet invisibly, transvisibly
                tenuously to be seen
And held, caught in the present by gleaming, growing facets.
Hardly a thing for buttons or celery.

For pearls--a nice contrast in texture, but they're not practical.
Pearls of bath oil to burst into bubbles as
              irridescent as glass?

Better to hold something born of nature (as itself)
              but the work of artists (as itself).
A fine pinot chardonnay trumpeted in tall fluted glass.
A mysterious amontillado pooled in a generous Irish crystal palm.

A precious fine edge on this cut?
The Waterford men who sweat at the kilns
              and sit at the grinding wheels
Would honor their goblet with a foaming amber brew.

Marjorie E

Mrs. William J. Ellis

Old Smoothie

Bring home fresh buttermilk.
Chill; pour into stemware.

Buttermilk is better in Waterford
Crystal. Honest.

Citrus Cooler

Fill a polished Waterford snifter with ice cubes. Add two shots of lime-flavored vodka and mix with carbonated grapefruit beverage. Garnish with slice of lime.

— Experience temperature drop.

The Thompsons have enjoyed participating in your contest. Our appetites for Waterford have truly been whetted.

Sincerely,
Sandra Thompson
408 Orchard Dr.
Marshalltown

Adam's Revenge

Pour equal amounts of chilled orange juice and cranapple juice into goblet. Splash in one teaspoon grenadine.

Garnish with apple slice dipped in lemon juice.

Nice on a cool eve!

AH-H-HHH... what _would_ _I_ do
with a _pet_ WATERFORD goblet?

let me see...

Find a dozen sparkling uses
Share my a.m. breakfast juices –

Hold a fresh picked flower cup
AS I clean my garden up!

Sit with me in summer shade
Sipping icy lemonade...

Perch upon my boudoir shelf
As I face
my other self

Hold melon balls at lunch for me –
All green – and peach – So frostily

WHEEEE!

Swing like a dazzling
sunshine ray –
Caught in a web of
macramé'!

MY connoisseur of heady wine...
In the evening when I dine –

Celebrate this birthday
liar –
With ONE pink candle all a fire!

Wink at me thru brandy glow –
when the hearth is burning low.

At my bedside thru the night,
Holding watch and ring just right!

ZZ·ZZZZ

Hmm-mm........m...m

Now that's my "someday-
life-to-be"...
When liesure catches up to me

For now, dear WATERFORD, my pet –
No glamour in your days as yet!

You'll never know a closet shelf –
You'll share with me as a "mirror-self."

Hold my ale – my mountain-red
My nightly milk beside my bed –

My cotton balls and unpaid bills
And water when I take my pills...!

Wherever you can serve me most
That will be your daily post.

Oh, well —
We may never share the silly dream,
Of the teaparty life I sometimes
Scheme —

There's joy enough in the pastel hue
From the rainbow captured
inside of you!

If only one idea came
to mind .. my pet
Waterford would swing
in a cobwebby net
of misty macrame'...
catching sunlight —
holding tiny ivy in water
— or six white daisies —
and at the Holiday season —
tiny, shiny balls of color!

Ms. Jan Jasperson

Dear Gentlemen;

Creating an interesting drink requires the titilation of the human senses, not the least of which is sight., Despite its obscured infrequency, the POUSSE CAFÉ, more than any other drink enhances just that. Ironically, on a busy night, creating a POUSSE CAFÉ is both a bartender's nightmare and his exquisit masterpiece. This stratified rainbow of sensual colours is only enhanced by a fine pristine lead crystal vessel.

A POUSSE CAFÉ is a series of liqueurs, gently poured into a narrow, somewhat straight sided glass, such that each ingredient forms an individual layer. These liqueurs are not mixed — consequently it is sipped with a straw.

HOW TO MAKE A POUSSE CAFÉ:

Grenadine	(red)	non-alcoholic
Creme de Cacao	(white)	50-54 proof
Creme Yvette	(violet)	55.5 proof
Creme de Menthe	(green)	60 proof
Galliano	(yellow)	80 proof
Brandy	(amber)	86 proof

Pour in the order given, at consistent or varying amounts. Top the brandy with a dab of whipped cream. To make the cream pink mix it with a few drops of Creme de Noyaux.

The object is to pour the densest liqueurs first, so that they float one upon the other. This is painstakingly achieved by slowly pouring each liqueur over the convex side of a spoon, so that it carefully runs down the inside of the glass, gently resting on the previous layer. Often if a liqueur is poured out of order it will separate and gradually seek its own level of specific gravity.

There are numerous POUSSE CAFÉ recipes — but the one I have submitted will offer the least chance for variation in densities. Most recipes call for 1/6 ounce of each liqueur for bar-sales purposes but the amounts used and the width of each strip may be varied to offer variety. Keep in mind that in most cases, the higher the liqueur's alcoholic content, the lower its density (lighter). But this does not always **prove** true. Whatever the case, it certainly proves a fine drink to end the evening with — that is, if you can find a nimble bartender that is patient enough.

Yours truly,

Robert W. Lanza
Mixologist
Bar Instructor

Gentlepersons;

In response to your beautifully photographed "Man lives not by water alone." advertisement, in the March, 1977 issue of Gourmet magazine, I am prompted to divulge a particular pleasure of ours:

It has long been my contention that the rich beauty of a fine brandy-snifter, conceived to concentrate the aroma of warmed brandy, more than simply being a sole-use tradition, would equally delight the pleasureable aroma of hot tea ... served in the, if you insist, "old Russian style", in a "glass", as opposed to a cup. Thus, a "brandy-snifter" has become one of my heightened delights, for enjoying a strong, richly-aromatic, beautifully burnt-amber-colored tea, "mixed" in the following manner:

Brew your favorite blended tea, in our case an Orange-Pekoe and Cut-black Pekoe, strongly, in the traditional tea-pot way (always pre-warming the pot with boiling water, then emptied, to receive a teaspoon of tea per cup of water, the actual brewing water being brought to a boil only from freshly-drawn water, never any from the hot tap, but only cold, which has not been allowed to lose its "oxygen" from over-standing.) and strain thoroughly in the pouring.

Pour down a pre-warmed snifter...and that, no finer than a cut-patterned Waterford crystal... into which one has already made to con

EDITOR'S NOTE: Although Don Saye obviously takes care when he takes tea in a brandy snifter, Waterford warns of the real risk of breakage if you pour hot liquids into its crystal.

tain powdered ~~~~~~ ~~ste (dissolution is thus much fas ~~~~re immediately servable, with little stirring required). One should leave a silver teaspoon in the glass, while pouring, to save heat-shock causing glass breakage "shock". As we like either milk (not cream) and/or lemon in tea, one is left with a quick choice at this stage. In using milk, it is a pleasure to only "float" a tablespoon of milk into the top of the tea. The warmth of the snifter, to the hand, the color of the tea, being slowly and subtly clouded by the softly "falling" milk into the depths of the "clear" beauty of the tea, to the eye, the steaming pungency of the aroma, concentrated just

to the nostrils by the smaller rim of the snifter; all make the actual savoring of the brewed tea a climax of palatable pleasure. The best afternoon can only be enriched, thus, and the worst afternoon unquestionably improved upon. I heartily recommend it!

As good bread deserves the honor of being broken in the hands, among loved ones and friends, so does a fine tea deserve the beauty of being "seen", as well as tasted.

Thank you, for the opportunity of sharing one of life's little, but treasured, delights.

Yours truly,

Don Saye

the inspiration for a best-seller :

a novel of political intrigue in which
a code message leading the protagonist
to hidden Nazi treasure is hidden in
microdots imbedded in the deep etchings
on the side of the goblet

(stand back, Helen MacInnes!)

I would loan it to my favorite minister for
use as a baptismal font.

I would place it under the leak in the ceiling
and tell my guests the total production is an
exciting new art form.

I would use it as a lure, as in "Lady with
Waterford goblet desires to meet gentleman
with equally discriminating taste".

To send to the government
and tell them to seal it
in A time capsule and
to instruct futher
generations as to what
class ment in the
bicentennial.

I'd arrange some flowers in it from our yard, and place it on my husband's chest of drawers, where each morning as he takes his glasses off the top of the chest, he would see the flowers in the goblet, and enjoy them at close range.

Why, you ask?

Because he has had one cataract operation, and is due to have another, and cannot and will not be able to see far enough in the out of doors to see and enjoy things. In using the beautiful goblet, filled with flowers I'd be bringing beauty close up for him to see and enjoy.

Sincerely,

Mrs Romonda M. Coverstone

IT'S CRYSTAL CLEAR THAT WATERFORD IS A YEAR ROUND AFFAIR "BOTTOMS UP"

JANUARY	NEW YEAR'S EVE	CHAMPAGNE
FEBRUARY	VALENTINE'S DAY	LOVERS DELIGHT COCKTAIL
	WASHINGTON'S "	CHERRY BRANDY
MARCH	SAINT PATRICK'S	IRISH WHISKEY
		CREME DE MENTHE SHAMROCK
APRIL	EASTER	WHITE WINE
MAY	MOTHER'S DAY	PINK LADY
	KENTUCKY DERBY	MINT JULEP
	MEMORIAL DAY	ROOT BEER
JUNE	FATHER'S DAY	SCOTCH*RYE*BEER
	WEDDINGS	ORANGE BLOSSOM CHAMPAGNE
JULY 4th.	INDEPENDENCE	(FREEDOM DRINKS*YOUR CHOICE)
	DRINKS	HARVEY WALLBANGER*STINGER*GRASSHOPPER*SHOT
AUGUST	V.J. DAY	VICTORY HIGHBALL
SEPTEMBER	LABOR DAY	SCREW DRIVER*BOILERMAKER
	SCHOOL	MILK*ORANGE JUICE*COCA COLA
	JEWISH NEW YEAR	MANISCHEWITZ
OCTOBER	COLUMBUS DAY	AMARETTO*GALLIANO*ANISETTE
	HALLOWEEN	CIDER*BLOODY MARY*BLACKBERRY BRANDY
NOVEMBER	THANKSGIVING	CRANBERRY JUICE*ROSE WINE*CORDIAL
DECEMBER	CHRISTMAS	EGGNOG* HOLIDAY PUNCH*PEPPERMINT SCHNAPPS
		SNOWY WHITE CREME DE MENTHE

Submitted by,

HELEN MOTTA
(MRS. S. D. MOTTA)

Only yesterday did I notice your advertisement in the 14 March issue of The New Yorker calling for goblet ideas and although the closing date was given as 1 May, I hope this entry is not to late for you to consider.

I am a chemist & the enclosed sketch illustrates the setup I use in the laboratory to synthesize a simple chemical substance called azomethane. This compound is a gas formed from other chemicals which are mixed in the flask shown. A stream of helium is used to push the azomethane into the cold traps where it freezes and is stored until it can be transferred to a vacuum system for purification and permanent storage. The excess helium is bled into a WATER-FILLED GOBLET and the helium pressure is adjusted until a steady gentle bubbling is achieved. Thus, the WATER and GOBLET ACT AS A SIMPLE PRESSURE REGULATOR.

Incidentally, since azomethane is destroyed by blue light, this procedure is carried out in dim red light, practical but exotic- an ideal setting for one of your fine goblets.

Sincerely yours,
Anne M Thompson

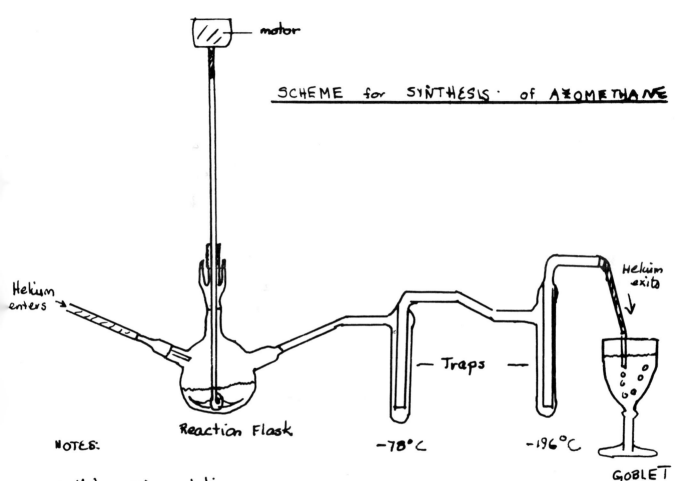

motor

SCHEME for SYNTHESIS of AZOMETHANE

Helium
exits

Helium
enters

— Traps —

Reaction Flask

−78°C

−196°C

GOBLET

NOTES:

1. Motor stirs solution.

2. Except for motor and rubber tubing (in shaded tones) all equipment is made of glass.

3. Traps are immersed in dewar flasks, which are what lines Thermos bottle. A mixture of alcohol and dry ice is −78°C; liquid nitrogen is −196°C.

Water, water everywhere
But not wherein you think.
In my goblet Waterford
There's something that goes "plink".
Leave others to thier piggy banks
Or passbooks fat and slick.
My dimes and quarters to the brim
More quickly do the trick.

A savings bank that's just first
    class
Is what I've made my Waterford
    glass.

CRYSTAL DELIGHT

The unsurpassed grace of daisies, carnations, roses, too,
Daffodils, baby's breath and hyacinths of blue,
Exquisite flowers radiantly in bloom,
Will by their presence enhance my room.

A breathtaking spectrum of harmonious hues,
Truly a cure for the occasional blues.
Nature's miraculous work -- a perfect piece of art,
Displayed in the vase that captures your heart.

The beauty of Waterford crystal has many an elegant style,
Blown by mouth and cut by hand by masters of the Emerald Isle.
Glistening in brilliance every facet untold,
From generation to generation it's a treasure to hold.

It's ageless beauty, no equal in sight,
Increasing in value -- a collector's delight.
Like nature's wondrous display of art,
Waterford, too, has played its part
In creating another work of art.

                                        Ann M. Heiselman

Kusam Jai
Raj

age: 6½

l,
so ready to
are my

use your Water Ford decanters the
guests will keep the same waterford
Goflet all evening + get refill
from waterford decanter

Sincerely
Mrs Clinton Ward

78   Mr. waterford — glass belongs
to ____?

mrs waterford g a belongs
to ____?

Well, I use colored pencils alot, and I'd
put all my pencils into a Waterford goblet
and think how beautiful the colors looked
    sparkling through the crystal glass.
J. McInerney

What would I pour into legendery Waterford crystal?

I would pour brilliant rhinestones to the brim of a
Waterford Goblet, tie a red ribbon around the stem,
and send it by messenger to Mary, love-of-my-life..
along with the following note:
Dear Heart: The only treasure I have to offer is
this Waterford Goblet. Place it on your special
shelf as a reminder that one day, the "diamonds"
will be real and the Waterford set, complete !

        as ever yours,

        Ross

        Ross Adams
        Santa Barbara, California 93105

Fran Rizzardi

The myriad facets catch the light

a rainbow of reflection

Any addition would be a blight

on its pristine perfection

Before the fire on a winter's night

I'd watch the crystal gleaming

To sit and ponder- sheer delight

the Waterford Goblet's for dreaming.

If I Held.

If I held
An Irish crystal,
Within my fragile
Grasp,
I'd share it
With the Leprechaun,
Who oversees
My task.

I'd polish up the goblet,
When I had
Drained it
Of its grape
And
The sun to sparkle
And the Leprechaun
To gape.

Then that Leprechaun
Who lives here
Would leap
Into repose
Inside that Irish crystal,
Which lately
Soothed my nose.

And he,
Who's into
Prying
Would focus
Both his eyes
And utter observations
Which I would
Swift record --
His every fascination,
Word by word.

The world
Would come
To comprehend
The specialties
He saw,
The wonders
That he witnessed
With the sharpness
Of his eyes,
Through those
Brilliant Irish facets,
Twice his size.

Eiku

Crunch a waterford goblet at
a Jewish wedding.
Anne Rubenstein

A Waterford Goblet could be used to house a unique electronic digital clock. The circuitry would be powered by small batteries, and the timing frequency would be derived from an electronic crystal. (An electronic crystal inside a crystal glass !!) The display would be light emitting diodes (LED) or a liquid crystal display (LCD).

As an electronic engineer I know this project could be easily built. (Digital clocks are a hobby of mine.)

VINCENT ELARDE

A drink for the President at lunch:

> Two crushed aspirins,
> Mixed thoroughly with Maalox
> To be followed by a refreshing chaser
> of Alka-Seltzer.

For the President before dinner:

> A delightful LEAD CRYSTAL BULLET --
> One double portion of vodka,
> Mixed with one double portion of gin,
> On the rocks --
> One shot and troubles turn into joy.

Both drinks, of course, served majestically in the
glittering brilliance of Waterford crystal.

Respectfully,

Waterford Crystal Garden
P. O. Box 1159;
Rancho Santa Fe, CA 92067

Dear Sirs:

As the poem describes, I come, at a distance, from
Ireland; my mother, my relatives, and all my
maternal ancestors are from there. Just last summer I
visited the country I had thought of as mine since child-
hood. I cannot say that I was surprised by anything we
saw, except that the land was more green than imagination
had allowed, that the sea was more constant, that the
silence was more complete than mind could have guessed.

We bought in Ireland two of your Waterford crystal
objets d'art, a pot for jam or honey and a small vase for
flowers. To us, my mother who had come from Ireland and
I who had come to her, crystal uniquely symbolizes Ireland.
What else could be so strong and yet so delicate,
outlasting men themselves, so clear and yet so many-faceted?
At home, the glass reminds us of ourselves, of our
origins, of our trip, of a way of life that is more in
balance than any other we know: with the strength to
endure and the transience of all beauty.

Now I put Peace roses from our garden into the vase and
orange honey into our jar, and there is an added measure
of beauty and grace to the best of our lives here. We
also think about the name "Waterford". A ford in the
water, a connection between two masses of land? For
those of us in the New World, who wish to maintain our
ties with the Old, the beauty that we live with in this
land reminds us of the beauty that comes from another.

Yours very truly,

Patricia C. Alley
Patricia C. Alley

The Irish Vase

"I am of Ireland," sang Yeats, and so am I.
Mother, mother's mother, great-grandmother,
Aunts and uncles and all those others who
Came from a green land, from a place sea-circled,
Where the lush meadow climbs to a green hill.

You see clouds there, piled extravagantly,
Cloud upon cloud, moving, shifting, great ships
Of air, and the sky opens like an egg
Split to infinite circumference, as the wind
Blows silence, and the light turns pearly-grey.

It is different here. Here, in California,
Where my people never thought to be.
Here it is dry, and here the wind blows no
Clouds. Here the sun stands still without the loved
Oscillation upon the changing sea.

It is a dry land, baked hard, and I long
For water, for sea, for rain, for foliage,
For that with elemental clarity.
This glass provides. Faceted, pure, light-carrier,
Strong and perishable, like its own land.

I have given her poppies from my desert
And the oleander that grows on our roads,
And they are beautiful, both in themselves,
And in her, for there is water here and
Light and many facets to be revealed.

                                        --Patricia C. Alley

"IMAGES"

The folks of the cities who worship the sun,
find solace and comfort in seeking some fun.
They hustle and bustle and rush through their days.
Living for weekends, never changing their ways.

How silly to think they must live life so quick.
If only folks knew of my fantastic trick.
I can travel anywhere any time that I choose,
Escape from frustrations, angers and blues.

Gee whiz you might say, "she has money to burn,"
But I'll tell you my secret if you care to learn.
I'll never get bored with my positive cure.
My Waterford Goblet so fine and so pure.

I go to the mountains and climb to the top,
or sail the great seas never wanting to stop.
The sun shines on reds, blues and the greens,
on all of Life's colors that were meant to be seen.

I go to the valleys and lay on the ground,
sunlight is fading, spreading darkness around.
The moon and stars make it possible to see,
Life's goals and ambitions are precious to me.

Each etch in the glass has become a new road
When everyday systems and tensions overload.
Make believes not only for childish schemes,
But building for today and tomorrows dreams.

My escape takes minutes, maybe ten at most,
but oh, what a spirit I'm able to toast.
No vacation ever can match this pleasure.
Yes, Waterford Crystal, I truly do treasure.

Legend or history - for when we speak of days so ancient as the dawn of the Galactic Age the two are so intertwined as to be indistinguishable - has it that the first Waterford decanter to leave the solar system was aboard the unmanned probe Voyager 84 which journeyed past the worlds of the gods Jupiter, Saturn, Uranus, beyond outermost Pluto and into the wine-dark depths of interstellar space. The decanter had been placed aboard the probe as a message to whatever spacefaring races it might encounter on its millenial journey: that the fashioners of the probe were not merely fabricators of technological marvels, but also creators, who fusing the elements of Earth, Air, Fire and Water, could unite Beauty and Function. The path of Voyager 84 is not known with sufficient accuracy to be traced now. If it has not yet passed its message to another intelligent race, it may yet do so, travelling from star to star, past red giant suns, past suns which are violent violet globes of light, through planetary systems lit by lambent green explosions of lumescence, past the myriad lights of ten thousand differently colored suns reflected and refracted by the crystal decanter fashioned in an Emerald Isle in legendary times: crystal worthy to outlast Time and the Galaxy.

-excerpt from "Waterford Decanters"
Encyclopedia Galactica
206th Edition, 6119

Crystal Lament

"I can't afford a Waterford,"
My darling cried. The Blackstairs heard
And threw the sob back to a bird

Who shrilly brogued a Gaelic chord,
"She can't affard a Waterford
And Cavan crystal leaves her bored."

The wailing bounded through the yard,
"It's just too much; she can't affard
To buy the best. And times is hard."

"We'll sell the calf, we'll sell the hog.
We'll sell the peat that's in the bog.
We'll pawn our sweaters, brave the fog.

"We'll pawn the kettle off the hob.
And if we need another bob,
We'll hire out--you'll get a job.

"We'll buy no Paddy, Jameson,
Old Bushmill, Dunphy--our spending's done.
Our poteen we'll sell to anyone.

"And if we must go into debt
To get the money for that set
We will. I'll have that crystal yet. "

In black dismay I caught each word.
I love you, dear, and Waterford.
But love or no, this is absurd.

I'll barter Father Matthew's bust.
I'll sell, I'll pawn, and if I must
I'll go to work to quench your lust.

But one thing's sure (and understood)
I won't stop drinking (even if I could)
For no damn crystal's <u>that</u> damn good.

Waterford Crystal

by Sandra Garceau

A lonely lily grew along side of a corn field.
Winter was on its way.
The lily could feel the ground tighten
  around its roots.
Soon it would be covered under a layer of icy
  cold snow.

Its leaves trembled with the very thought.
The lily felt a warm sensation as a kind hand
  picked it from its cold bed and placed it
  within the security of a Waterford Crystal Vase.

A light shone through the vase and reflected
  upon the petals of the lily.
The lily felt honored to be in such a perfect
  piece of art.
The sides of the vase twinkled brilliantly
  like a cluster of snowflakes.

The lily - a perfect creation of nature -
  had found its equal.

Gentlemen:

In March of 1966, I was seriously injured in a car accident. Five weeks later, on April 22, the president of the airline for which I worked, was killed at the controls of one of our planes along with 87 young soldiers. As an executive, I spent hours at the crash scene.

The first and only time this has happened in aviation, we were faced with a battle of survival. In spite of excruciating pain and a paralyzed arm, I continued working to help save the airline instead of taking time off for medical treatment.

Scheduled months before either accident, was an aviation ball at the local Press Club. I was chairman. Somehow, in spite of my work and pain, I got it all together. Dressed in a jeweled gown, I attended the ball as though nothing had happened.

Driving to work the following morning, exhausted, in horrible pain, grief stricken over the crash, my shoulders were sagging under the weight of my world. As I walked into my office, I was at the point of giving up. Then, I saw the flowers.

A perfect red rose bud, an open rose, green foliage and ribbons in a sparkling Waterford vase reflecting the rays of the morning sun. Sitting in the center of my white desk, the beauty was breathtaking.

The florist's card was simply signed, "From a Constant Fan". Though my secretary called, the idenity of the sender was unknown.

Words can't explain how much that gesture meant to me! Somehow, I managed to "keep on keeping on". Today, over 11 years later, the vase brings a smile of rememberance.

And how does one press a rose? In the heart, of course.

Sincerely

Ruby Hickman

My figure was chubby,

My legs were quite stubby,

Such features no artist would ink;

Till a goblet I filled

With a liquid - first chilled,

Giving class to a diet-food drink;

Then for months I drank them,

Now I'm thin as a stem

On a WATERFORD GOBLET - I think;

So it's "crystal clear"

To make fat disappear

Put your dreams in its beauty and "CLINK!"

Well, the first idea involves a few set Waterford goblets. By taking a few W. goblets with different heights and designs you could line them up in an aquarium to form a waterfall! You could obtain a small water pump very cheaply and have it pump water to the highest W. goblet. By slanting each one, and possibly even adding on a spout for draining to the next one, you could built a really decorative indoor waterfall for your livingroom. You could also add other odds and ends to decorate the waterfall, such as rocks, plants, etc.

The second idea I had in mind was to put a small decorative gyroscope inside two W. goblets. You would set one Waterford goblet

upssidedown on top of the other one. (right side up) Then you would fasten small anchors to the top and the bottom so that it would secure the gyroscope. When you set it on the window sill you would get an amazing light show from the suns rays shining through the Waterford designed goblet and the spinning gyroscope.

I read that you are selecting 100 winners so I'm giving you my ideas and I hope you find them as stimulating and original as I found you advertisement.

Sincerely,
Steven Quinn

100

A flower -

    fragile, delicate.

Alone it is like a newly born deer,

    lost from the rest of the herd -

    weak and insignificant.

But a flower coupled with Waterford Crystal

    Is like thunder paired with lightening:

    Strong and Powerful,

    Glowing with light, beauty, and hope.

Dear Sir
I'm going to enter
your contest. If I
had a Pet Wat-
erford crystal
I would set
it in ~~there are toy things~~
the middle
of my elec-
tric train
board)

and I would put
smoke pellets in
it.

Sincerely,
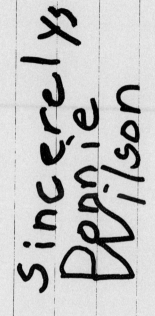
Bennie Wilson

St. Louis, Mo.
63130

Vessel for reading tea leaves

In the morning, rainbows
dance in the crystal glasses:
you bring me rainbows for breakfast
in Waterford goblets on a tray.
On the cold nights
we spoon thick peasant soup from them,
and pretend that we're royal.

Oh, we fill our crystal with love
and with memories. Once, for my birthday
you gave me a glass, and the tiniest puppy
that I'd ever seen peeked over the rim.
Once, in the spring, a glassful of bright
silk ribbons to tie in my hair. In August
you gave me a goblet of mist from dry ice
and you said, "Here's a soft Irish morning, m'love."
For Christmas, an ivy
from Thoor Ballylee, potted in the stemmed glass.

Oh, I would give you goblets of snow
with maple syrup to swirl in designs
for candy, the way you did as a child.
In the spring I would bring you
tadpoles, we'd watch through the crystal facets
as they changed into frogs
or princes. I'd bring you
a glass filled with grasses and clover
so you could smell the outdoors,
and a goblet of rainwater to pour on your hair.
Every cool autumn, I'd fill it with leaves,
a glass full of flames to sit by your bed,
and deep in December, five golden rings.

Oh, we fill our glasses
with love, and with memories.
We fill them with dreams,
and on each star-like glimmer
we make a wish.

A Water Orchestra
(to play Handel's "Water Music", of course)

Hamburg, New York 14075
April 20, 1977

"Filled With Happiness"

I would fill it with sunshine on cold
winter days.

I would fill it with love and use it
all ways.

I would fill it with fire from a
candle so bright.

Reflections of dashing and
stabbing bright light.

As my grandmother dear, so very old,
Put silver teaspoons for the glass to hold.

As we waited to choose, we'd look
with wonder
At her beautiful Waterford cut glass tumbler.

A handful of shamrocks all pink
or all white,
They nod and they bow come the
morn and the night.

I would fill it with moonshine
From Cork to the stem
Waterford goblets, each one is a gem.

— Martha R. Eder

Ladies and Gentlemen:

A water goblet by Waterford is indeed not for water alone. I took a piece of my Waterford into the darkroom with me and exposed 5"x7" sheets of Kodalith film to light from the enlarger passed through the crystal.

And here's what I got in my entry entitled "Images by Waterford."

Hope you enjoy it as much as I enjoyed doing it.

Sincerely,

Teresa Garland

Teresa Garland

IMAGES BY WATERFORD:

FORMED IN THE DARKROOM BY PROJECTING LIGHT FROM A
PHOTOGRAPHIC ENLARGER THROUGH CRYSTAL ONTO FILM.

PATTERN: LISMORE
FILM: KODALITH ORTHO TYPE THREE
LENS: f/22
EXPOSURE: 4 SECONDS
DEVELOPER: KODALITH A+B;   1-2 MINUTES
ARTIST: TERESA ANN GARLAND

You ask what I would serve in legendary Waterford crystal? Why, a _legend_, of course!

Several years ago I had my introduction to Waterford in a most unorthodox manner. While visiting with my boyfriend's relatives in the quaint, New England town of Kingston, Rhode Island, we decided to pack a picnic lunch and enjoy the beaches of that area.

My boyfriend George's Aunt, with whom we were staying, was certainly no slouch when it came to picnic lunches. All neatly packed in an enormous wicker hamper were a checkered table cloth, hard-cooked eggs pickled pink in beet juice, fresh fruit, delicious sandwiches on home-baked bread, cheese, white wine and Waterford crystal wine glasses. THAT'S RIGHT!! WATERFORD CRYSTAL WINE GLASSES! FOR THE BEACH YET!!!

Needless to say, I was immediately taken with the beauty of Waterford, and seeing the glasses for the gems that they were, asked politely if they weren't a bit costly for mere picnic fare. The reply George's Aunt gave me I shall always remember: " If you have something you enjoy, it should be used regardless of the cost. If you feel a thing is too good to be used often because it is costly, chances are you shouldn't have it in the first place!" Well, I've never forgotten those words. As a matter of fact I decided on the spot to someday own my own collection of lovely Waterford.

And today, slowly but with determination, I'm acquiring a set of the Waterford pattern, Kenmare. I love the fact that Waterford has a cherished heritage and is truly an investment as it grows more valuable with time. But what I love even more is _USING_ it and enjoying the hand-cut beauty that is so uniquely Waterford.

As to what beverage to serve in Waterford crystal? I repeat: Serve a _legend_. For anything from a picnic to the most formal of dinners will truly become a legend when graced with the memory of elegant Waterford crystal.

I would think it vitally important to make sure that the first Americans to settle on the moon take Waterford goblets with them. After all, <u>how</u> can civilized man expect to enjoy his first taste of moon water if it is not drunk from a similar celestial, shining object?

Anne McCaskill

My nine-year-old daughter was frighteningly ill last
winter, with a persistent, lingering kind of
pneumonia. By the time I got home from the office,
my wife was exhausted, so I tried to take over as
nurse and babysitter.

I'd bring a funny little gift from the drugstore
downtown. We'd find a favorite bedtime story to
read. And then I'd go through the ordeal of
getting that sick little girl to take her medicine,
a thick white liquid with an unpleasant minty flavor.

Eventually we found the way, by making a ceremony
of it. We'd toast better days or Winnie the Pooh
or summer at the beach or the Fonz. Each night a
different toast. But what made it really special
was the Waterford crystal wine glasses we used in
the toast, a treat my little girl appreciated as she
carefully "clinked" glasses with me.

The medicine didn't always go down perfectly, but now
as the end of the school year approaches, she is
fully recovered, the pneumonia belongs to her long-time-
ago history, and the Waterford on the china cabinet
shelf is part of the legend that parents like to
remember.

                              Sincerely,

                              Maurice Heffner

For Sally's Wedding, With Love

Alas, I do not like a shopping spree
Where I'm too stunned by crowded fancy shows
And stacks of things and things which frighten me;
Give me a shop like Shreve and Crump and Low's.

A velvet fold enshrines a gleaming **vase**,
A lambent light on every facet shone.
My eager hand slides forth to hold and raise
The **cynosure**, delighting me alone.

The cool and satin glass I quickly hold,
My fingers tell me what my eyes have known.
I'm happy as an oil sheik with his gold.
For little Sally: "My how she has grown."

The Waterford outshines her silver's rays
And for this uncle, deep and touching praise.

Earl F. Cook

```
Chocolate Mousse,
Pate de Goose.
Sturgeon's eggs
and froggie's legs.
Strawberries, blueberries, raspberries, plum
and 13 kinds of sugarless gum.
Leibfraumilch, Mateus Rose,
And '59 Mouton Cadet.
Golden earrings might be nice,
or freshly made Italian Ice,
bananas sliced,
apples diced.
Comice pears
to put on airs,
shrimp in sauce
... and dental floss.
```

When your Waterford goblet
is no longer one.
Mobile the fragments and
        capture the sun.

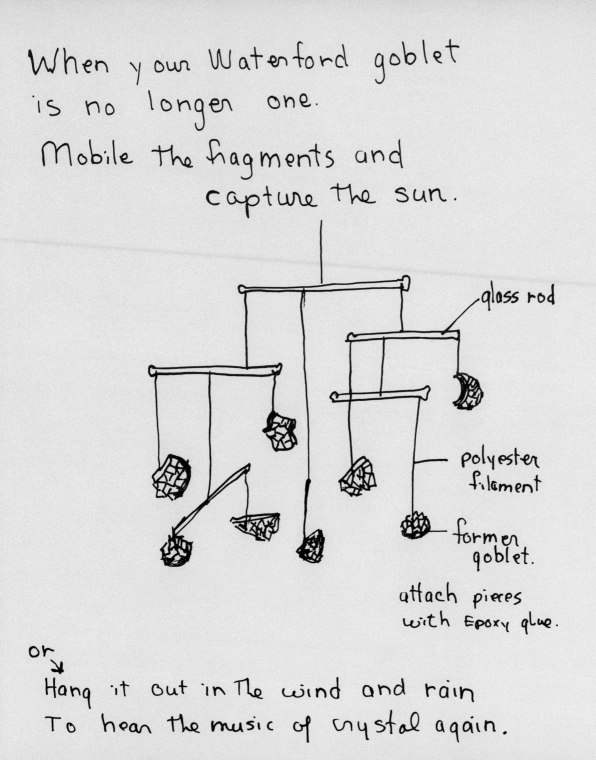

glass rod

polyester
filament

former
goblet.

attach pieces
with Epoxy glue.

or
Hang it out in the wind and rain
To hear the music of crystal again.

In Africa, my homeland, we have the
custom, when friends are gathered to
rejoice in the birth of the first-born,
of filling a glass with a bit of the
finest wine and then pouring a few
drops onto the ground. How lovelier
the gesture became recently when the
wine was poured from our sparkling
Waterford cyrstal goblet in honor
of our first child!

Black Minnaloushe

2 oz. blackberry flavored brandy
Club soda
Wedge of lime

Pour into Waterford Crystal Goblet

... Minnaloushe creeps through the grass
Alone, important and wise,
And lifts to the changing moon
His changing eyes.

from William Butler Yeats
"The Cat and the Moon"

Submitted by: Sharon Stephens
Nan Temple

ODE TO A WATERFORD GOBLET
by the Rev. Harold T. Lewis

When the Almighty created grains of sand
Did He anticipate the day that hand
Of man would take those fragile particles
To make so many useful articles?
To sand man added lime and ash
To form the substance known as glass.

Beakers, vials and panes galore
Created the craftsman by the score;
But, sated with all these things of duty
Decided to make a thing of beauty.

So then, from first, the element fire
He molten glass extracts;
With steady hand and skillful jowl
A lovely shape exacts;
And, next with chisel deftly cuts
Each delicate impression,
And sets goblet on the cooling shelf
Until another session
When with the self-same care and time
He'll create a goblet more sublime.

For this our craftsman deserves a mortarboard!
He's created a signed, original Waterford!

120

Well, here's what you do:

On a beautiful summer day you get yourself a
piper.   He sits cross legged in the garden and
he plays a gentle tune on an Irish tin whistle.
The sound is as clear and crystalline as a Waterford
goblet.   Hummingbirds come from far and near to
listen and to drink the nectar from the flowers.
Now, this piper is a leprechaun (sp.?) and he
bewitches the hummingbirds with his song and they
give him the nectar which no one else has ever
tasted.   When the sun begins to set and the birds
go home, the piper has a tiny goblet of the sweetest
most precious liquor to be found on this earth.
That's the drink I'd pour into the legendary
Waterford crystal.

Dear Sir or Madam:

In your advertisement of February 27, 1977, in the New York Times Magazine, you asked, "What would you pour into this legendary Waterford crystal?"

I would pour into it the most famous and highly reputed wine ever produced in antiquity, the wine from the Falernian district near Capua in Italy.

Galen, the court physician to the Roman Emperor Marcus Aurelius (161-180 AD), wrote that Falernian wine, which came in both dry and sweet varieties, was ready for drinking after ten years and good for drinking from fifteen to twenty years. Athenaeus the late second century AD polymath called Falernian the pleasantest wine in Italy.

The legendary vintage of Falernian was bottled in 121 BC, the year Opimius was consul in Rome. This vintage was served more than a century and a half later at the most famous and lusty (but fictional!) banquet in antiquity, Trimalchio's dinner party. Trimalchio was a creation of the Roman author and voluptuary Petronius, who for a while was a favorite of Nero (54-68 AD). This character Trimalchio was the supreme ancient example of the "success story." Born a slave, he gained his freedom and proceded to acquire farmlands. By the time he reached old age, he possessed all the land from Naples to Sicily. He remained a cultural low brow but was generous and enjoyed having and serving only the best. Thus at his banquet he served unspecified vintages of Falernian early in the evening. But to cap the night, Trimalchio had his servants bring out sealed glass jars whose labels read, "Falernian of Opimius's vintage, 100 years in bottle." As everyone gaped at the label Trimalchio cried out, "Ah me, so wine lives longer than miserable man. Wine is life."

Archaeologists have not found any of this fine drink. But should they discover an ancient jar, ought it not to be decanted into and drunk from Waterford crystal?

Sincerly yours,

Herbert Abramson
Steinmann Professor of Classics

122

Wedding Day

by

Barbara Brown

Jenny glanced over the long table
  Wedding presents stacked high,
    Gifts that rushed her
      To grow up—
        Fast.
Then her eye caught a rainbow,
  shimmering prisms of light
    coming from the tall bud vase.
It held a single rose
Its petals just opening,
  pink,
    delicate,
      beckoning.
The card read:
    Jenny dear,
    Your Grandfather gave me
      This Waterford,
        long ago,

on our first anniversary.
  'Beauty holds beauty within,
  A perfect pair,' he said.
Remember his words
And share them
  with your first granddaughter,
  on her wedding day.
    Love, Grammy
Jenny lifted the vase,
Its contours
  strong and smooth.
Beauty holds beauty within,
A perfect pair.

A Water Goblet by Waterford Is Not For Water Alone

The best suggestion that I can imagine is to use a water goblet by Waterford to make an object of art. Many kinds of objects could be made to decorate the inside or outside of a house or a park. For instance, one could surround his house with a wall or a fence made of water goblets by Waterford. See below, an illustration of my idea.

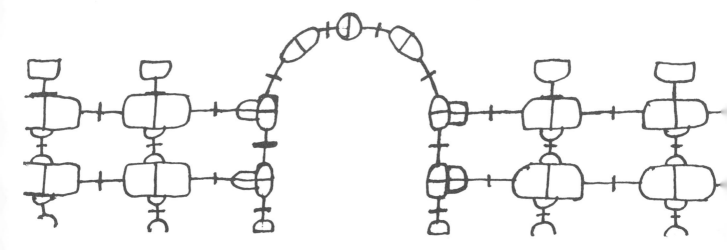

Submitted by Junichi Nakajima ___Junichi Nakajima___
(signature)

Gentlemen:

In my youth, good crystal was always linked to tradition.

During the summer months, my mother would buy fresh cherries, place them in a clear gallon jug and then pour either brandy or whisky over them until the jug was full. She then placed the jug in the cellar "to season" -- until the cherries absorbed the whiskey or brandy.

It became a tradition at festive ocassions for all guests, children included, to be served several cherries in my mother's best crystal. The children were served the cherries soaked in mild brandies, while the grown-ups were served the whiskey soaked cherries with "a mouthful" (about 1/4" in the bottom of the glass of whiskey or brandy. These whiskey-or brandy-soaked cherries were the best appetizers I have ever known and, of course, were followed by sumptuous meals.

As a child, I felt grown up when I was included in such festivities. As a grown-up, I looked forward to these occasions.

So what would I put in the Waterford crystal? Several soaked cherries with a mouthful of brandy or whiskey.

Sincerely,

Dino A. Brugioni

DEAR SIRS:

THE IN REPLY TO YOUR ADVERTISEMENT,
INT NEW YORK MAGAZINE, (DEC 27, 76 - JAN. 3. 77):
BELOW ARE MY REPLYS TO,

PRI WHAT WOULD YOU (I) DO WITH
AT WATERFORD GOBLET ?

1. TAKE IT TO THE TAJ MAHAL
AND TOAST TO THE LOVE OF MY
DARLING !

2. I'D SIT ON MT. EVEREST AND
PARTAKE OF A STARLET! (STAR ETC.)

3. GIVEN IT TO SOCRATES, AND HE
WOULD HAVE WRITTEN A SONNET !

4. SAT WITH CEASAR ON THE
RUBICON AND SAVORED HIS ACCOMPLISHMENTS,

5. HELPED IN THE BUCKET BRIGADE
AT THE GREAT CHICAGO FIRE !

6. FILLED IT WITH ICED WATER
AND POURED IT DOWN CHICKEN
LITTLES COLLAR !

HERE'S HOPING,

I'd fill it with mints
I'd drape it with grapes,
With strawberries, cherries
And candies*------all shapes.

I'd fill it with dressing
Or sauces or dips
Or even with caviar
If I were rich.

I'd "stalk" it with celery
Or peppermint sticks,
Iced coffee spoons ,
Or hors D'oeuvre picks.

I'd fill it with violets
Or one perfect rose,
My pearls and my earrings,
Some swank "quelque choses."

I'd use it for golf balls
White, shiney, and new;
For favorite keepsakes
And trinkets to view.

And when it was empty
And sparkling and clear,
I'd fill it with bubbling
Champagne or cold beer.

In a previously owned sportscar, I had a rather ingenious system, In which I used a waterford gablet.

I placed a 1 3/4" hole in the dash, and a mount inside, so that a bottle of wine would protrude approx. 2 inches into the passenger compartment. On its top was a small chemists valve. An extra line from the air-conditioning kept the beverage cold.

In the console between the seats was a foam lined compartment, containing 2 gablets. Long travel thirst? Yuies!

It was one of the main selling points of the car.

If I win, I shall soon have a set of four gablets in my present sedan.

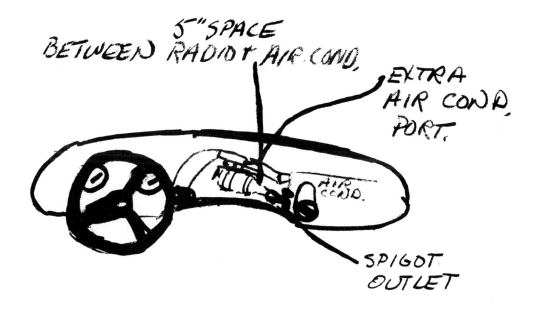

5" SPACE
BETWEEN RADIO & AIR COND.

EXTRA
AIR COND.
PORT.

AIR COND.

SPIGOT
OUTLET

JAMES P. BAKER

A Peck O'Maut

"We are na fou, we're nae that fou,
But just a drappie in our ee;
The cock may craw, the day may daw,
And aye we'll taste the barley bree."

~ R. BURNS

Pour—

1½ ounces of
Scotch

1 pony of
Drambuie

Ice
Water & Stir

MEMBER OF THE CLAN MACLEOD

Nora C. McCabe

My suggestion of something to pour into legendary Waterford crystal is a drink from a soon to be legendary state, the state of Georgia. This drink is PERSIMMON BEER. So far as I have been able to determine, this recipe has never before been printed, although it is well tried.

Persimmon Beer (a recipe as told to me by a native Georgian who had enjoyed the drink as an after school refreshment in her youth)

First you get a little keg (a 5 gallon one) and in the bottom you put clean straw. The straw must come up above the bung hole as it will serve to drain the liquor. Bake some sweet potatoes and a pone of corn bread. Break these foods up (including the skins of the potatoes) and distribute in the bottom of the keg.

Gather one-half gallon of ripe persimmons. Be sure they are ripe, a condition usually assured after the first frost, as the taste is noted for turning the mouth inside out if the persimmons are green. Remove the burrs and add these to the bottom of the keg. Add about one-half dozen ripe locusts; break these up too and put in the keg.

Fill the keg with water and let the mixture ferment outside. The temperature outside should be between 60 and 70 degrees Fahrenheit. (This recipe, as you can see, is usually made in the fall when the persimmons ripen and the temperature in Georgia falls between these degrees.)

The resulting drink is a mildly alcoholic beverage of pure amber color, perfectly suited both to autumnal season and to showing off the graceful features of any Waterford pattern.

I sincerely hope that you will find this idea among your 100 most interesting ones.

Very truly yours,

Glenda G. Thompson

Glenda G. Thompson

SIRS

    I INTEND TO TAKE A GobleT, by WATERFORD, TO MY GRAVE SO THAT when my boNES ARe duG Up, EONS FROM Now, The GobleT Will show I WAS someone OF substANce ANd CLASS.

Our garden often grows in our Waterford cookie jar, much to the chagrin of the local cookie population. It's a much less fattening, but equally satisfying, treat when the (chocolate) chips are down.

Sandra and David Hunter

THE PET WATERFORD GOBLET.....

Like any pet, it should be held --
          to the sun
          to candlelight
          to the least glimmer of light,
Its perfect arc-rim catching fire.......

I would let it hold its fire,
The fire in which it was born,
The fire _for_ which it was made --
     catching light evanescent,
     incandescent brilliance.

I would count it wrong to even briefly hide
Its prismed perfection
Where all fires cool because/the light has died.

Not even for a little while would I have it
Cease its saying,

          "I am beautiful and I _will_ be,
           for I was moulded in fire
           and I carry now, forever,
           its heat, its force, its _light_...."

It was exactly three weeks ago today that my little girl Susie-Beth came running excitedly into the kitchen calling "Mommy!" I knew I was a goner already.

"Mommy! Can I —"

"Over my dead body."

"Mommy! Mommy! Please! Can I...?"

"Over my dead body, honey."

"Please!!! Can I have a pet?"

"You do, dear, your little brother Mikey is out back eating peanut butter on the swing set."

"No, mommy, I found it on the way home from school."

"What could you ever find on the way home from school that isn't rabid or derelict?"

"This!!!" exclaimed Susie-Beth as she held up a mud-covered object that resembled one of Mikey's feet, "Its name is Sherrie!"

"That's lovely dear, get rid of it."

Susie proceeded to burst into tears and turn bright red.

"Wwweeeelll...Let's wash it and see exactly what it is," I conceded falteringly.

"Oh boy!! I gotta pet!"

I washed the foot (or was it a potato?) and as the mud came off I felt a surge of excitement that must be likened to the thrill Dr. Frankenstein felt when he created life. To my amazement I uncovered an exquisite hand cut crystal water goblet that shone like all stars and diamonds shaped in the mold of a most graceful god. I was awestruck.

"Susie-Beth, your father and I have been talking and we've agreed it's about time you had a pet."

"Hooray!"

"But, you have to take very good care of it and never take it outside or remove it from the mantlepiece."

"I'll even feed it everyday."

"Susie-Beth, Sherrie doesn't eat, she only drinks. Your mother will make sure she stays healthy."

"Oh, thank you mommy!"and with that Susie-Beth gave me a great hug.

When Henry came home that evening I showed him the goblet and we decided it was only fitting to christen Sherrie with some vintage sherry. Henry ran down to the liquor store and we spent the evening getting pleasantly sloshed. The next day the Garden Club came over for coffee, but I just had to show off my new goblet, so I poured more sherry in it even if it was a water goblet. Sparkling red looked gorgeous with my new earrings anyway. The girls were just green with envy.

The next day my best friend Lydia came over and we enjoyed the sherry ritual together too. In fact, in the course of the next two weeks, my whole social life revolved around that sparkling water goblet. Not only did my social life revolve around it, but so did my domestic life because it definitely added interest to my cleaning to sip sherry while sweeping under beds, and you wouldn't believe how festive macaroni and cheese is with a dash or two of sherry. Oh yes, my head was doing quite a bit of revolving too. I began waking up constantly in the middle of the night, but with a little nip of sherry I was out like a light for at least another 30 minutes.

Well, it all started three weeks ago to this very day, and here I am, what was once a happily married woman, now living alone in the house with the liquor cabinet extension being added. My husband left me and divorce papers have been filed because he says I'm too "happy" these days or something like that, I couldn't really understand, he seems to mumble these days, I can never make out the words. Oh yeah, and little Susie-Beth said I could keep Sherrie, she has even forgotten that Sherrie was her's because we'd become so close and the Garden Club never seems to accept my invitations anymore, and the only time I talk to Lydia is if I call her up and she hasn't a plausible excuse for hanging up. In fact, we were talking the other day...or was it today?

"Oh Lydia, Lydia...umm...oh yeah, oh yeah, Lydia! Are you there?"

"Yes, (sigh)"

"Lydia, I'm so lonely! Just so lonely! Lydia, what can I do? (sob)"

"Why don't you get a pet? They say they make great company."

"That's it, a pet! I'll get a pet!! I'll go down to Freedman's Pet Store and I'll get a doggie or a kitty...or maybe I'll go check out Bullocks glassware department!...Lydia...?"

While I'm on Dr. Robert Linn's "Last Chance Diet," I have to
drink two quarts of water per day. I use the Waterford goblet in my
hat to drink that water, and make my diet repast more elegant.

When I reach my desired weight, the Waterford goblet in my
hat becomes a bud vase, so that I can always carry a fresh Oregon
posie with me!

Carol Ironside

Gentlemen:

I noticed the beautiful color photo of your Waterford crystal in a recent Sunday edition of The New York Times.

What would I pour into a glass of legendary Waterford crystal? I'll tell you what drink I'd pour into it, and I'll tell you why.

We have in our wine rack a bottle of Baron Philippe De Rothschild, Mouton-Cadet, 1970 given to us by friends. This is the year we bought our house here on Wolf Lake in New York's Sullivan County Catskill Mountains. We are saving this excellent Bordeux to drink on the day we burn our mortgage in 1995.

What better way to combine the best in crystal and excellence in wine than by pouring the one into the other, and then toasting a truly great family celebration, and a truly great crystal.

We're looking forward to this possibility.

Sincerely yours,

Harold R. Black

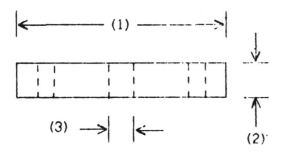

(1) Disk diameter same as foot of goblet.

(2) Disk height slightly more than turntable spindle height.

(3) Hole diameter same as hole in a record.

(4) Notches for rubber bands to hold goblet to disk.

LIGHT SHOW

Two of the distinctive features of Waterford goblets are their cut surfaces, in the bowl and the prism-like stem, and the optical clarity of their glass. These aspects can be exploited to refract and reflect light to provide a spectacular display. You need a narrow intense beam of light, a motorized stand, and a goblet. The best light source is a laser (small lasers cost about $100), but an opaque box with a strong light in it and a small hole in the side might also work. The motorized stand can be a phonograph turntable with a small wood disk placed on the spindle to hold the goblet (see sketch). Attach the goblet to the pedestal with rubber bands, start it turning at the slowest possible speed, and aim the light at the cuttings on the bowl or at the stem. The light will reflect and refract in moving patterns all around the room.

Sincerely,

Mark Birnbaum

Mark Birnbaum

Index

c) Sarah Sandell, El Cajon, CA
75. Ann M. Heiselman, Akron, OH
76a) Kusam J. Raj, Stamford, CT
  b) Margaret Eiseman, Scottsdale, AZ
77a) Charles R. Begeman, Grosse Pointe Woods, MI
  b) Jane Gustafson, Yakima, WA
78a) Vincent J. Grechen, Jr., Verona, PA
  b) Mrs. Clinton Ward, Mankato, MN
79. T. McInerney, Bayport, NY
80a) Ross Adams, Santa Barbara, CA
  b) Paul D. Naish, Cincinnati, OH
81. Mrs. Barbara Nakamura, Glendale, CA
82. Fran Rizzardi, Torrance, CA
83a) Madeline P. Eberhardt, Holiday, FL
  b) Diane K. Wilson, DeKalb, IL
84. Betty Luz, Lowell, MA
85. Betty Toth, La Puente, CA
86. Eiku, Deerfield, IL
87. Ann Rubenstein, Belvedere, CA
88. Vincent Elarde, Smithtown, NY
89. W. Giovanello, Columbus, OH
90. Patricia Alley, Los Gatos, CA
92. Kathy O'Neill, Novi, MI
93. Janet Engelmann, Butler, NJ
94. Prof. Harvey Abramson, Vancouver, BC
95. A. J. Solomon, Chinchilla, PA
96. Iris Simon, East Meadow, NY
97. Sandra Garceau, Whitman, MA
98. Ruby Hickman, Fort Worth, TX
99. Mrs. Julie Beyrouty, San Juan Capistrano, CA
100. Steven Quinn, Phoenix, MD
101. Mark Hammond, Whitman, MA
102. Donnie Wilson, St. Louis, MO
104. Jim Soo Hoo, Los Angeles, CA
105. Deborah D. Bennett, Baltimore, MD

106. Douglas Allchin, Timonium, MD
107. Martha R. Eder, Hamburg, NY
108. Teresa Garland, Roanoke, VA
112. Susan T. Duval, New Haven, CT
113. Anne McCaskill, New York, NY
114. Marvin K. Heffner, Manakin-Sabot, VA
115. Earl F. Cook, Marblehead, MA
116. Dianne K. Maripolsky, Flushing, NY
117. Roberta Elliot, Gainesville, FL
118. Mrs. Collis Bassey, Brooklyn, NY
119. Sharon Stephens/Nan Temple, Chicago, IL
120a) Harold T. Lewis, Washington, DC
  b) Betty Tiska, Syosset, NY
121. Mary Lu Walker, Corning, NY
122. Herbert Abramson, Lancaster, PA
123. Barbara Brown, Encinitas, CA
124. Junichi Nakajima, New York, NY
125. Dino A. Brugioni, Falls Church, VA
126. George A. Duhart, Washington, DC
127. Shirley Heifetz, Lowell, MA
128. James R. Baker, Sound Beach, NY
130. Nora C. McCabe, Savannah, GA
131. Glenda G. Thompson, Athens, GA
132. Paul E. Thiebaut, San Mateo, CA
133. Sandra & David Hunter, St. Paul, MN
134. Iris Simon, East Meadow, NY
135. Eleanor Bennett Convers, Gibsonia, PA
136. Lisa Waddington, Diamond Bar, CA
138. Carol Ironside, Portland, OR
139. Harold R. Black, Wurtsboro, NY
140. Robert J. Supino, Seattle, WA
141. Mark Birnbam, Pittsburgh, PA